World of Reading 1

Disney FROZEN

Anna in Charge

Written by
Elle D. Risco

Illustrated by the
Disney Storybook Art Team

Disney PRESS
Los Angeles • New York

Printed in China
First Box Set Edition, August 2016
1 3 5 7 9 10 8 6 4 2
FAC-025393-16127
ISBN 978-1-4847-7386-4

Queen Elsa is going
on a trip.
She will be gone for
a day and a night.

Elsa is leaving
Anna in charge.
She gives Anna a note
with tips for how to rule.

Anna waves to Elsa.
"It will be fine!"
she says.
"Do not worry."

Anna goes to her room.
She wonders what
Elsa has to say.

Anna does not have time
to read the note.
There is a knock on the door.

It is a guard.
Anna is needed to
solve a problem.

Two farmers are
having a fight.
They need Anna's help.

"His chickens get loose and
eat my corn!"
one farmer yells.

"His cow keeps eating
the grass in my field!"
says the other farmer.

Anna does not know
what to do.
She is not the queen!
Anna reads Elsa's note.

Problems can be
hard to solve.
You have a good heart.
Do what you think is right.

Anna thinks hard.
What *does* she
think is right?
"I have an idea!" Anna says.

“The chickens can eat the corn.
The cow can eat the grass.
You both can share
the milk and the eggs!”

The farmers agree.
Anna smiles.
She solved the problem!
Elsa would be proud.

Olina comes in.
There is a boat race starting.
One team does not
have enough people.

Anna reads more of Elsa's note.
I hope you are not bored.
Do not be afraid
to mix it up!

Anna thinks hard.
She has an idea.
She will help the team!

Anna goes
to the water.
She greets her new team.

Anna rows hard.
Her team comes
in second place!

Next Anna visits with
a group of children.
She is nervous.

Anna reads more
of Elsa's note.
You have a great big heart.
Use it to have fun.

Anna thinks of how
she and Elsa
used to play.

Elsa is right.
Anna does know how
to have fun.

The rest of Anna's
day flies by.
There are troops to inspect.

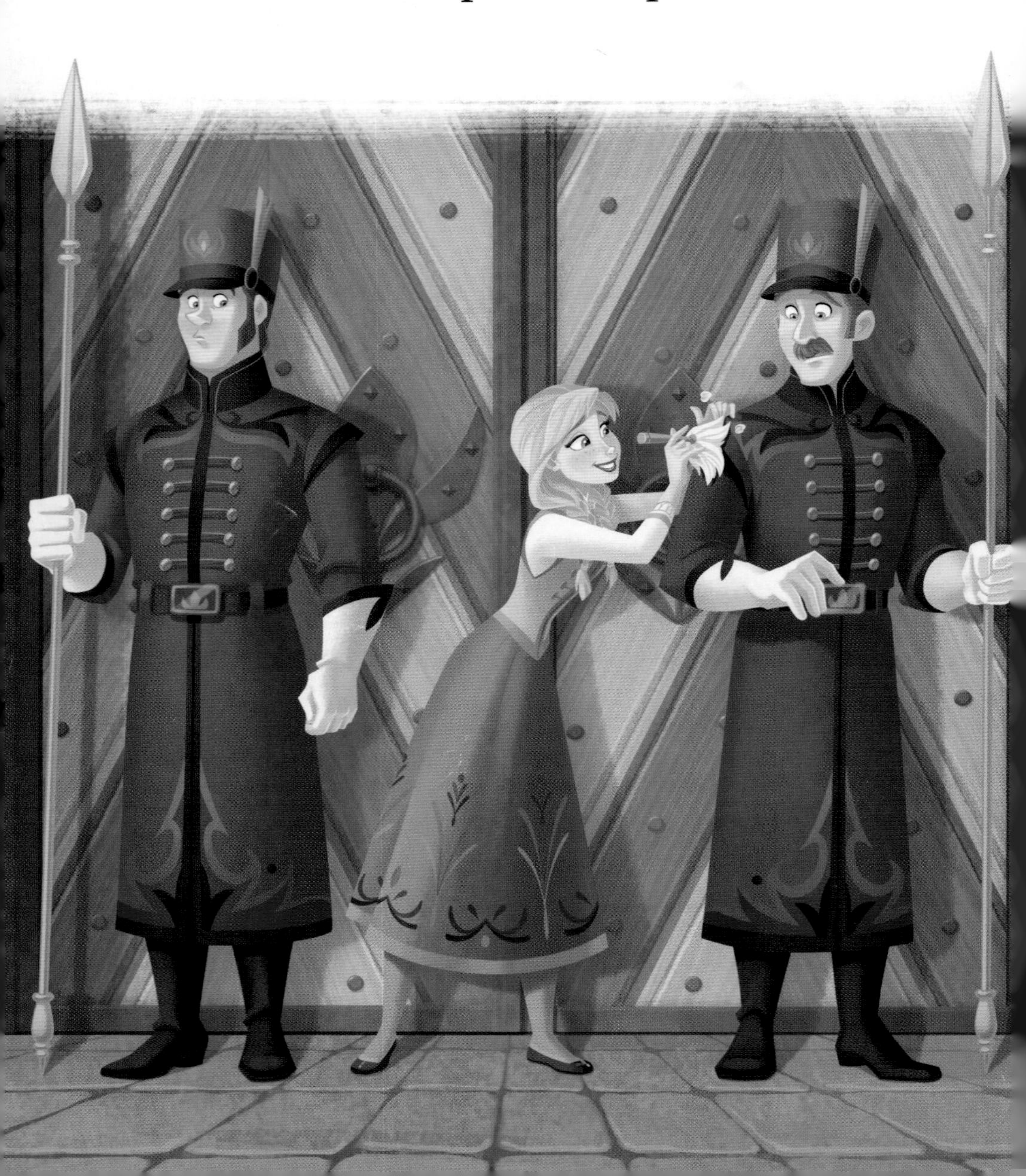

There are races to watch.
There are guests to greet.

By the end of the day,
Anna is very tired.
Elsa's note has
one more tip.

After a busy day,
it is nice to see the stars.
The best view
is from the roof.

Anna goes to the roof.
Elsa has left her
a picnic dinner
and a note.

Good job today.
You can step in for me anytime.
Anna gasps. She would not like
to be in charge *every* day.

Anna keeps reading.
But do not worry.
I will be back tomorrow.
Anna is glad!